GREEN GOLD ANIMATION PVT. LTD.
PRESENTS

in

THE RISE OF KIRMADA

The Movie

Created By: Rajiv Chilaka   Story: Darsana Radhakrishnan

BHEEM
THE HERO OF DHOLAKPUR

CHUTKI
BHEEM'S BEST FRIEND

KANHA
BHEEM'S FRIEND

RAJU
BHEEM'S CUTE LITTLE FRIEND

JAGGU
THE TALKING MONKEY
(BHEEM'S FRIEND)

KALIA
BHEEM'S RIVAL IN DHOLAKPUR

DHOLU & BHOLU
KALIA'S FOLLOWERS

INDUMATI
THE PRINCESS OF DHOLAKPUR

THE GENERAL OF DHOLAKPUR

SOLDIERS OF DHOLAKPUR

RAJA INDRAVERMA II
THE KING OF DHOLAKPUR

THE PRINCE OF MAANIKDESH

THE PRINCE OF JAAMNAGARI

THE PRINCE OF PORSINGHA

EAGLE

SOLDIER OF KIRMADA

FLYING SOLDIER OF KIRMADA

SHAITAAN
KIRMADA'S EVIL GURU

KIRMADA
THE EVIL VILLAIN

Chhota Bheem and friends are surprised to see
Krishna in Dholakpur. As per the wish on the king Indraverma, they
all set out to neighbouring kingdoms to invite them for the Food
and Might festival.

Meanwhile, Kirmada rises and gets more evil powers.
He is determined to destroy Chhota Bheem, Krishna and Dholakpur.
Can Chhota Bheem and Krishna stop Kirmada when he launches
a bitter war?

THEY ARE THE PRINCES OF DHOLAKPUR'S NEIGHBOURING KINGDOMS...

...MAANIKDESH, PORSINGHA AND JAAMNAGARI!

HMMM... THE OCCASION WAS CALLED THE FOOD AND MIGHT FESTIVAL!

TWENTY YEARS AGO, WHEN I USED TO BE FIFTEEN YEARS IN AGE AND AT THE POINT WHERE THE BORDERS OF DHOLAKPUR, MAANIKDESH, PORSINGHA AND JAAMNAGARI USED TO MEET...

...THERE USED TO BE A FAMOUS STONE TEMPLE...

...EVERY YEAR PEOPLE CELEBRATED A FESTIVAL HERE ON THE SECOND FULL MOON OF THE MONSOONS!

DURING THAT OCCASION...

...THE BEST WARRIORS OF THESE FOUR KINGDOMS SHOWCASED THEIR FIGHTING SKILLS!

THE PRINCE OF JAAMNAGARI WAS THE MOST AGILE IN FIGHTING WITH HIS MACE!

THE PRINCE OF MAANIKDESH WAS THE BEST IN ARCHERY...

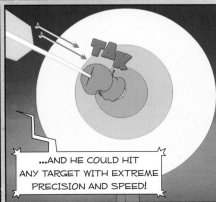

...AND HE COULD HIT ANY TARGET WITH EXTREME PRECISION AND SPEED!

* JALEBI : A DESSERT MADE OF SWEET BATTER DEEP FRIED IN THE SHAPE OF A COIL.
* LADDOO : AN INDIAN SWEET MADE FROM A MIXTURE OF FLOUR, SUGAR AND SHORTENING, WHICH IS SHAPED INTO A BALL

www.chhotabheem.com

* KACHORI : A PURI STUFFED WITH SPICED LENTILS, POTATO OR BEANS.
* DHOKLA : MADE FROM A BATTER OF GRAM FLOUR (FROM CHICKPEAS) COOKED BY STEAMING.

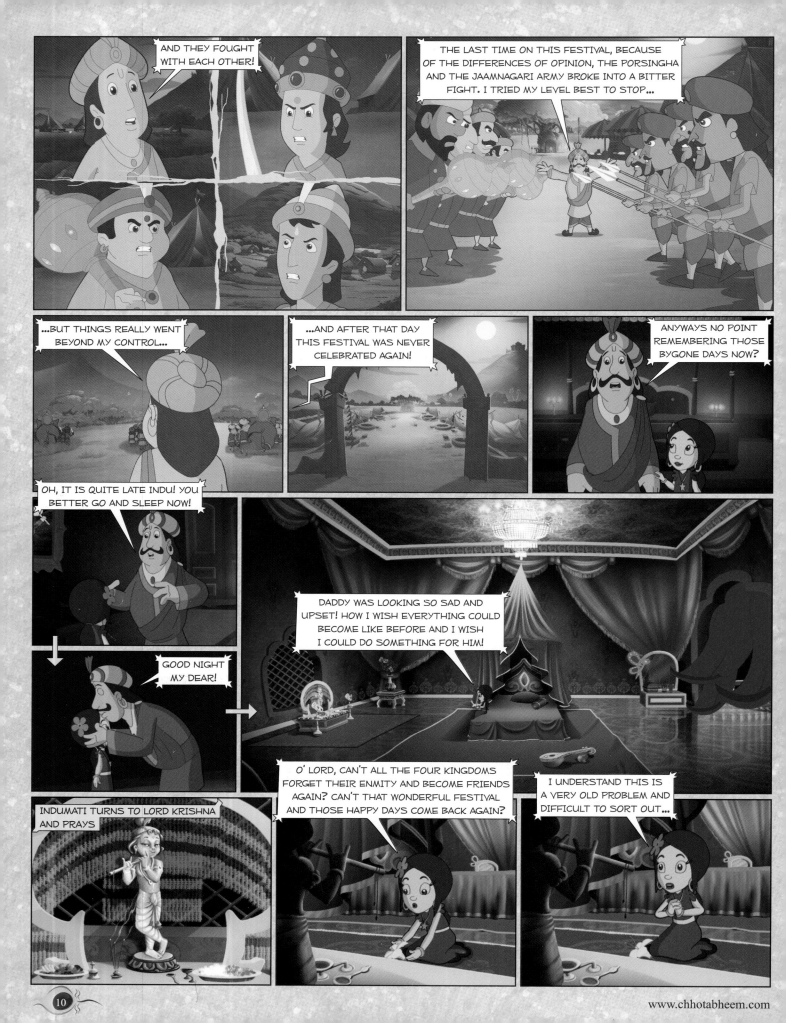

JUST THEN

HEY, THERE THEY ARE, DHOLU, BHOLU AND KALIA!

OH!!!

POOR DHOLU BHOLU!

LOOK WHAT I HAVE GOT FOR YOU GUYS!

WOW!!! LADDOOS!

BHOLU WATCH OUT!

BHOLU TRIPS ON A STONE...

...AND LOSE CONTROL

AWWWW!!!

THE BUCKETS OF MILK FALLS OF THE TRAY

JUST THEN BHEEM JUMPS AND DOES NOT LET THE BUCKETS FALL ON THE GROUND

IMPOSSIBLE!!!

WELL DONE BHEEM!

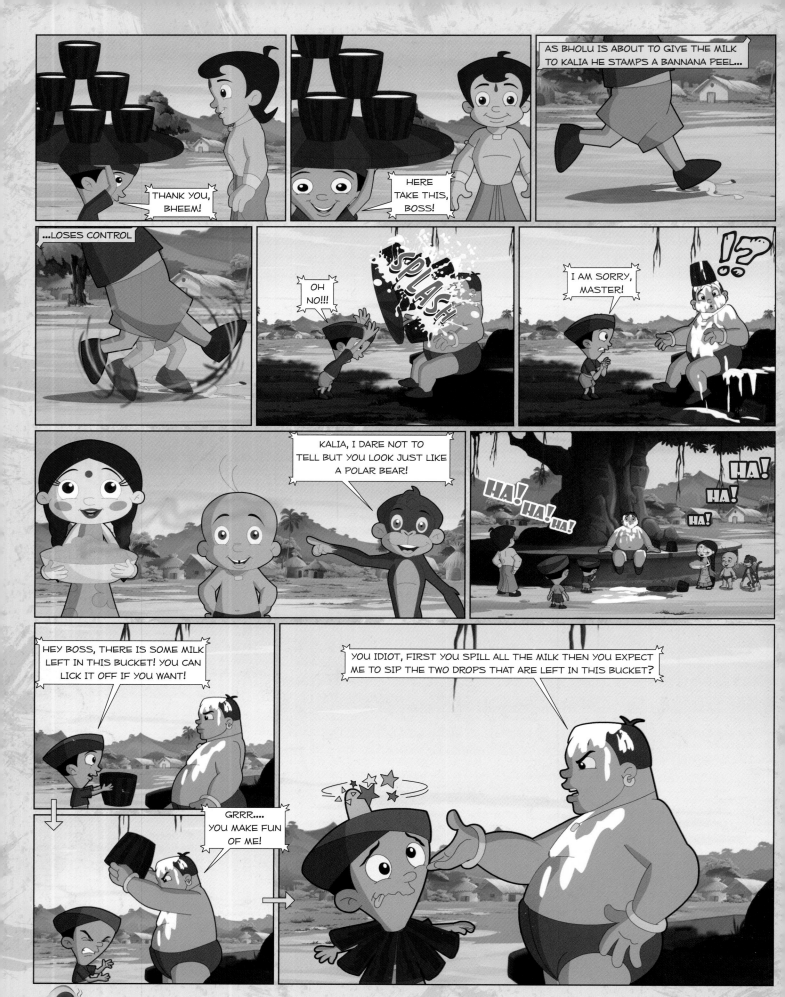

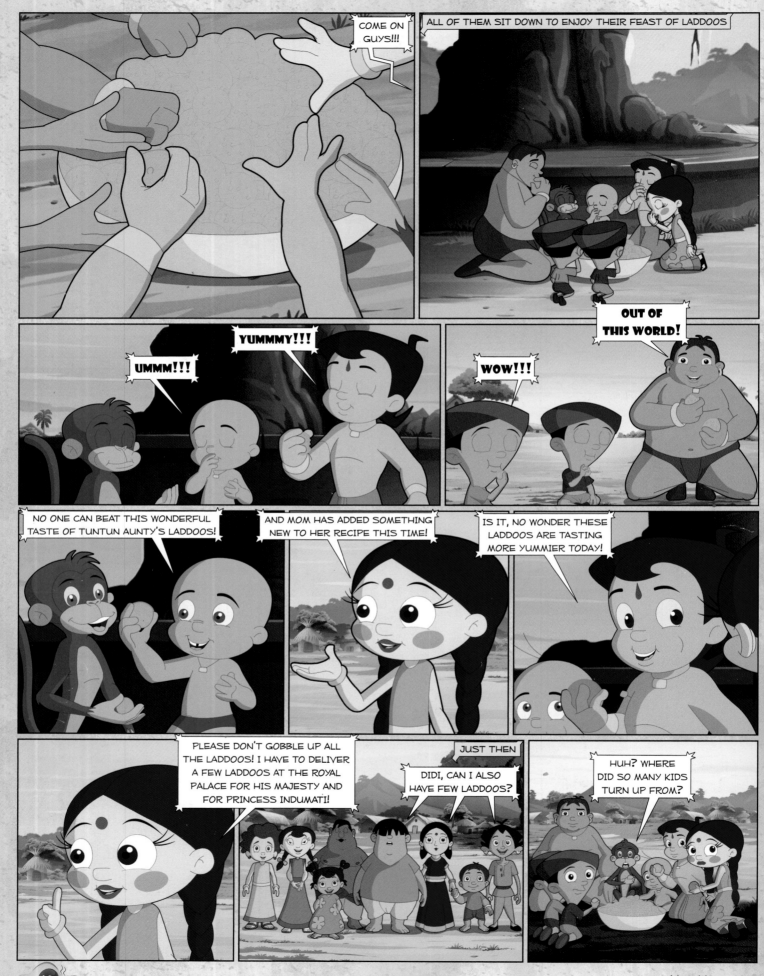

INSIDE THE TRAINING AREA

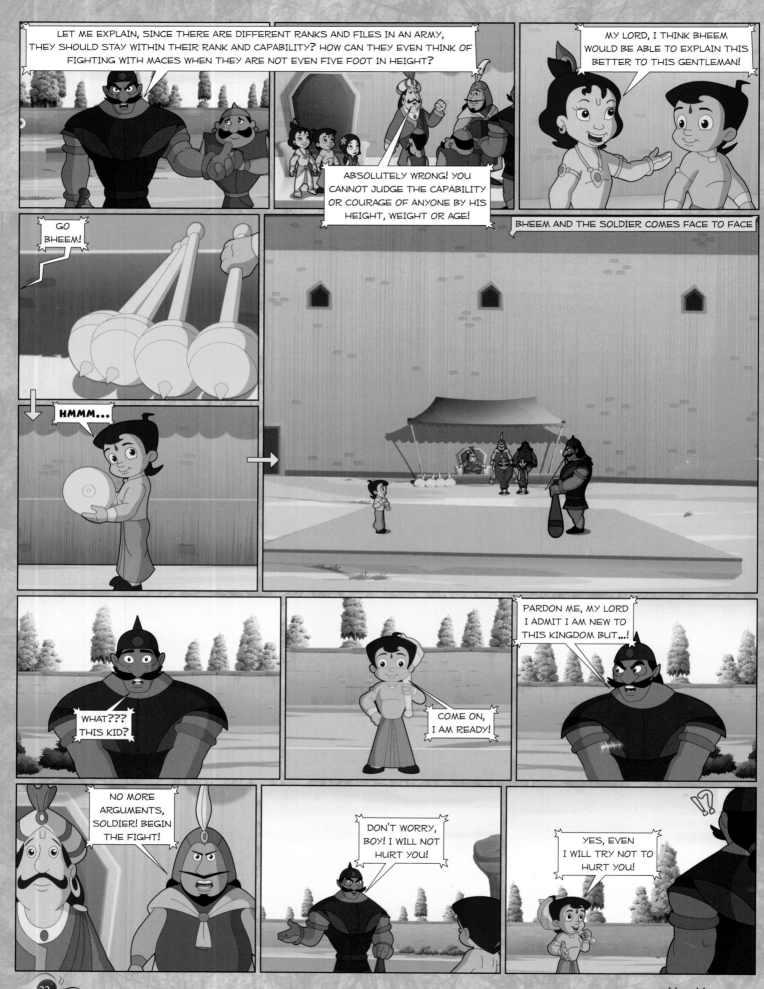

THANK YOU YOUR HIGHNESS!

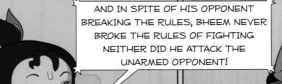

AND IN SPITE OF HIS OPPONENT BREAKING THE RULES, BHEEM NEVER BROKE THE RULES OF FIGHTING NEITHER DID HE ATTACK THE UNARMED OPPONENT!

YES, THAT IS THE SIGN OF A TRUE SOLDIER!

BHEEM IS DELIGHTED TO HEAR ALL THE PRAISES

WELL, THAT IS ENOUGH ABOUT WARFARE AND TRAINING FOR THE DAY! WHY DON'T YOU KIDS JOIN ME FOR A GRAND MEAL NOW?

WE WOULD LOVE TO!

OH SURE, MY LORD!

LATER INSIDE THE ROYAL DINNING ROOM

AAH!!!

SLURP

HEE! HEE! HEE!

SLURP

BHEEM AND CHUTKI RELISHES THEIR SWEET

SLURP

HMMM...

WHY ARE YOU LOOKING AT IT LIKE THAT, RAJU? THIS IS JELLY AND IT IS SWEET! YOU MUST HAVE IT WITH CUSTARD! I SIMPLY LOVE IT!

REALLY? THIS LOOKS SO STRANGE TO ME!

OUCH!

PLOP

HMPH! THAT IS NOT THE WAY TO HAVE IT RAJU! YOU WATCH ME AND LEARN NOW, OKAY

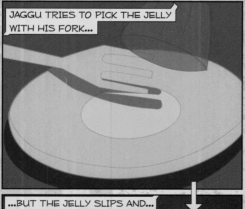

JAGGU TRIES TO PICK THE JELLY WITH HIS FORK...

...BUT THE JELLY SLIPS AND...

...GETS STRUCK ON CHUTKI'S NOSE

HUH?

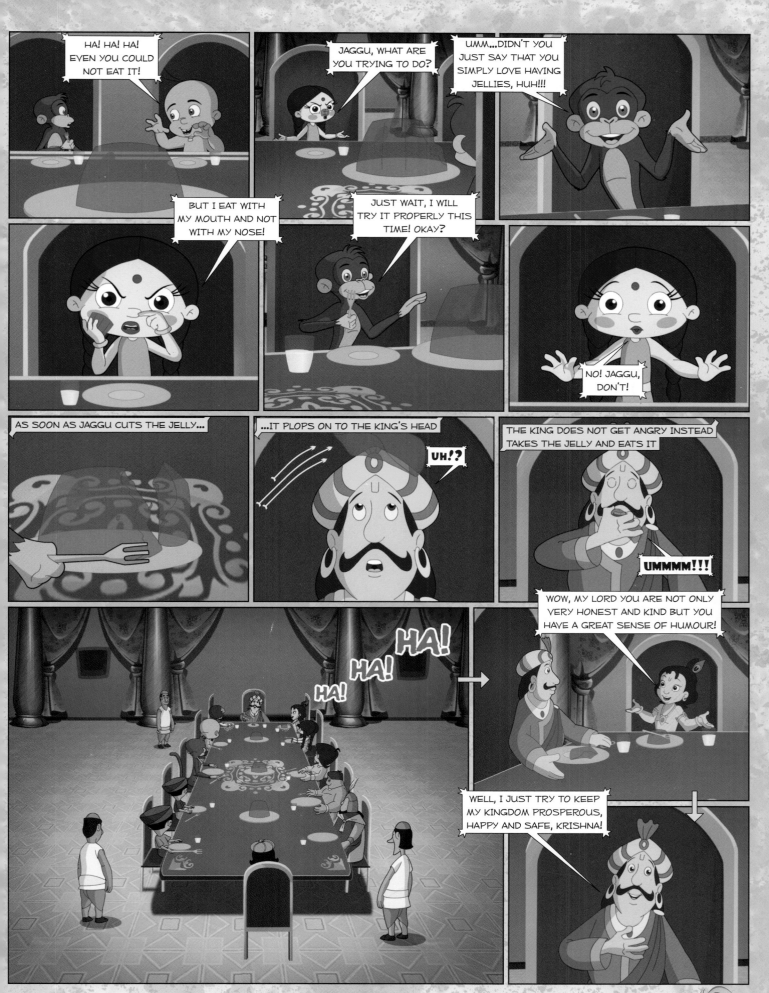

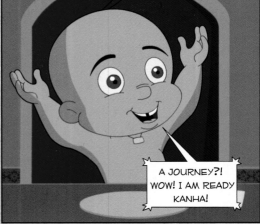

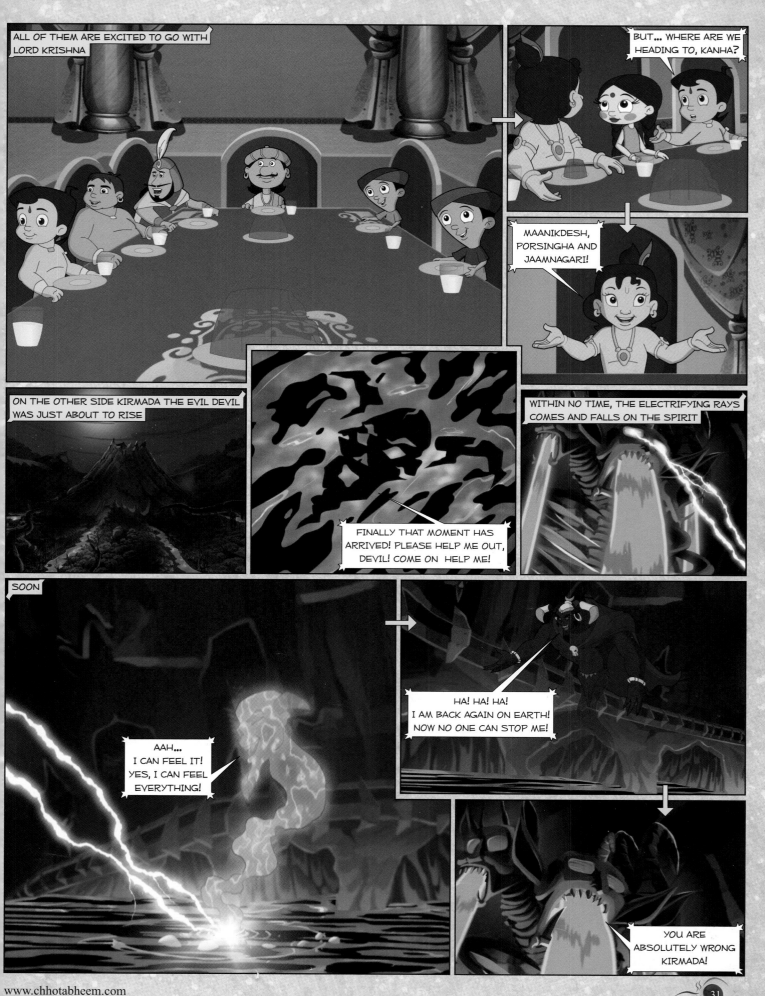

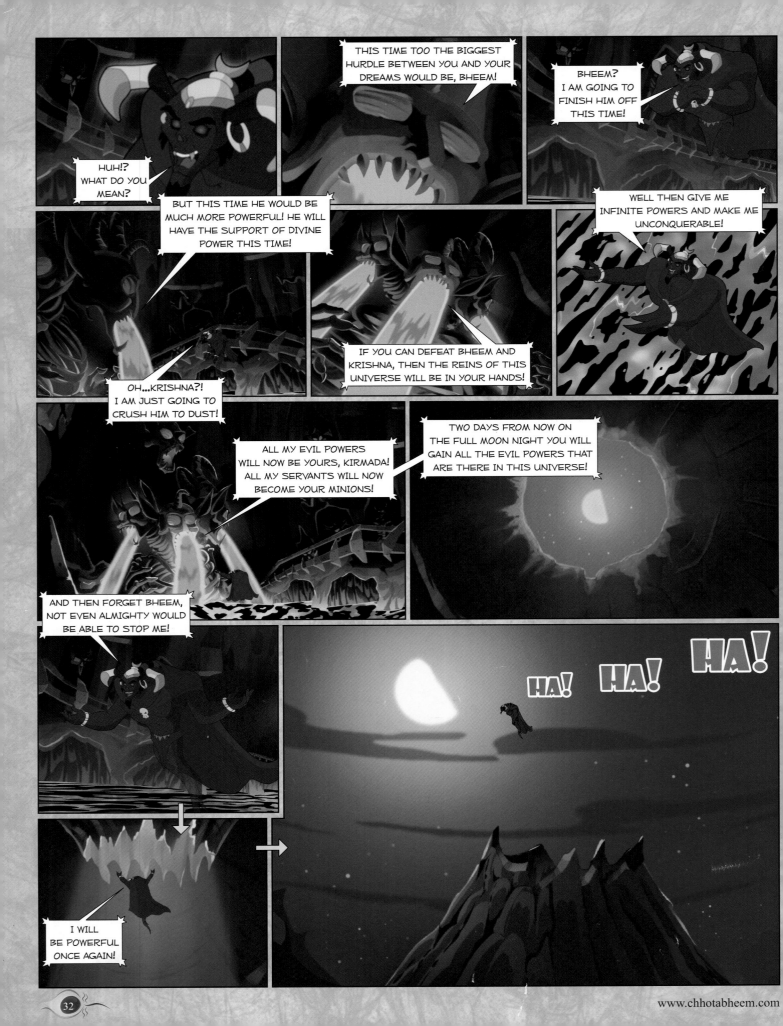

ON THE OTHER SIDE AS PLANNED, THE KIDS LEAVE FOR THEIR DESTINATION

KANHA, IS THIS MAANIKDESH?

YES BHEEM!

THIS PLACE IS FAMOUS FOR TWO THINGS!

AND WHAT ARE THOSE, KANHA?

THE ARCHERS OF THIS REGION AND THE JALEBIES!

WOW, JALEBIES!!!

ARCHERS?

IT IS SAID THAT PEOPLE OF MAANIKDESH ARE SO PERFECT THAT THEY NEVER MISS THEIR AIM!

JUST THEN

ZAAAP

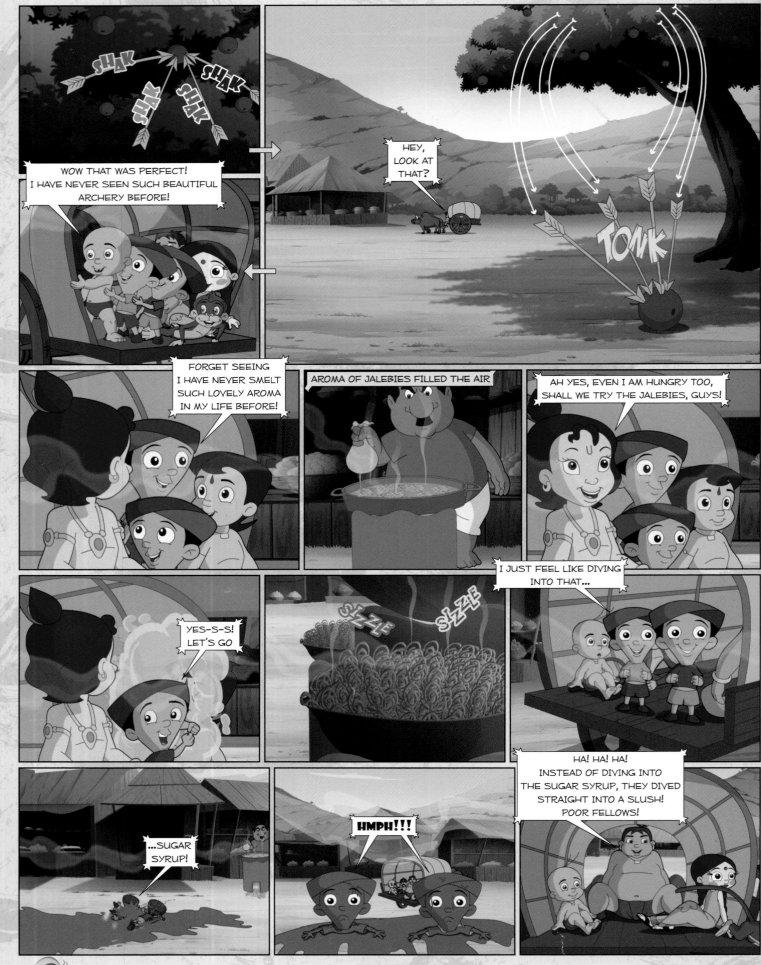

www.chhotabheem.com

PATH PUZZLE

Bheem and chutki wants to meet up but they cannot find the way!
Can you find the path which adds up to 21?

THEY SEE A FOUNTAIN AND STOP TO DRINK WATER

YAY! YAY!

GULP

MEANWHILE KIRMADA IS KEEPING A WATCH ON THEM

LET ME QUENCH BHEEM'S THIRST IN A DIFFERENT WAY!
HA! HA! HA!

JUST THEN KRISHNA SEES KIRMADA'S SHADOW IN THE WATER

HUH?

WHAT ARE YOU LOOKING AT, KANHA?

SOON KIRMADA RISES UNDERNEATH THE WATER...

...AND PUSHES IT TOWARDS THE WALL

BECAUSE OF HIGH FORCE THE WALL STARTS TO CRACK

KRACK   CREEK

HUH!?

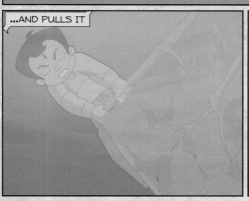

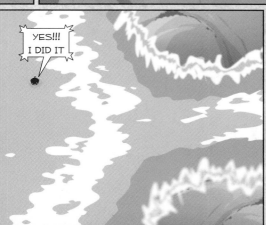

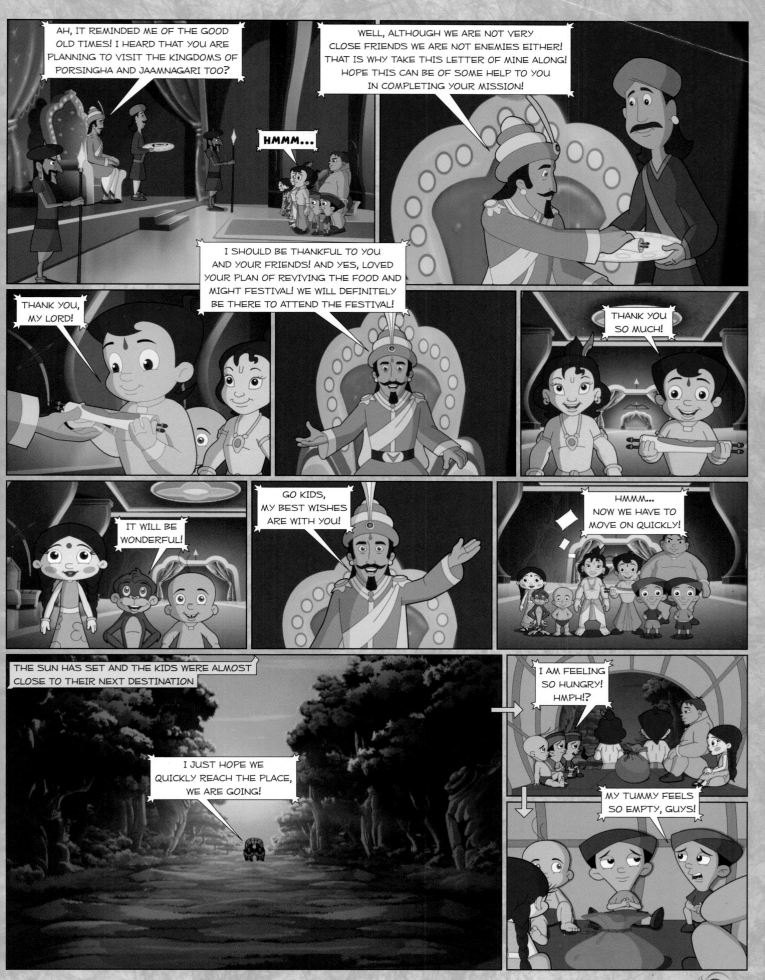

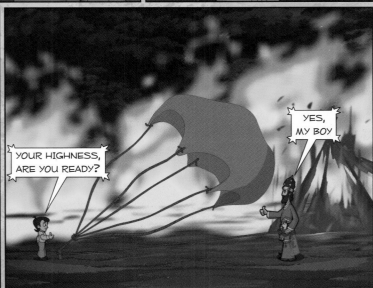

BHEEM LEAVES THE ROPE

HERE YOU GO!

OH GOD!!! I HOPE THIS WORKS

AND SOON THE KING AND THE PRINCESS GETS TO THE OTHER SIDE SAFELY

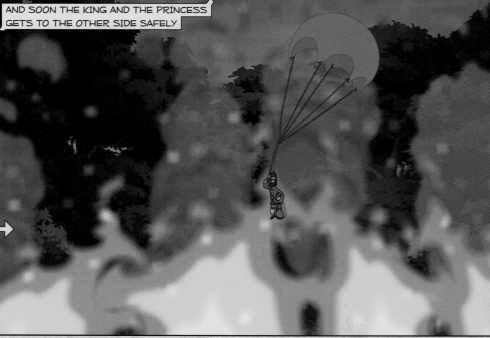

HEY, LOOK AT THEM!

BUT BHEEM IS NOT THERE ALONG WITH THEM?

HMMM...

JUST THEN OUR SUPER HERO JUMPS UP HIGH...

ALL OF THEM WATCH HIM IN AMAZEMENT

WOW

TAK

...WITH HELP OF A ROD

...SAFELY

BHEEM! YAAY! YOU DID IT AGAIN!

YES, BUT THE FIRE IS STILL OUT OF CONTROL!

I WILL TAKE CARE OF IT!

LORD KRISHNA LOOKS UP AT THE SKY AND IT STARTS RAINING

RUMBLE THUNDER

HUH? HEY, IT'S RAINING!

SOON THE FIRE SUBSIDED WITH THE RAIN WATER

HUH!? LOOK AT THAT, COULDN'T IT COME A LITTLE EARLIER?

DON'T BE GRUMPY, RAJU! INSTEAD WE SHOULD BE HAPPY THAT THE FIRE HAS ATLEAST BEEN PUT OFF!

WE ARE THE ONES WHO ARE HAPPY THAT WE MET SUCH A BRAVE BOY TODAY! WHERE ARE YOU FROM?

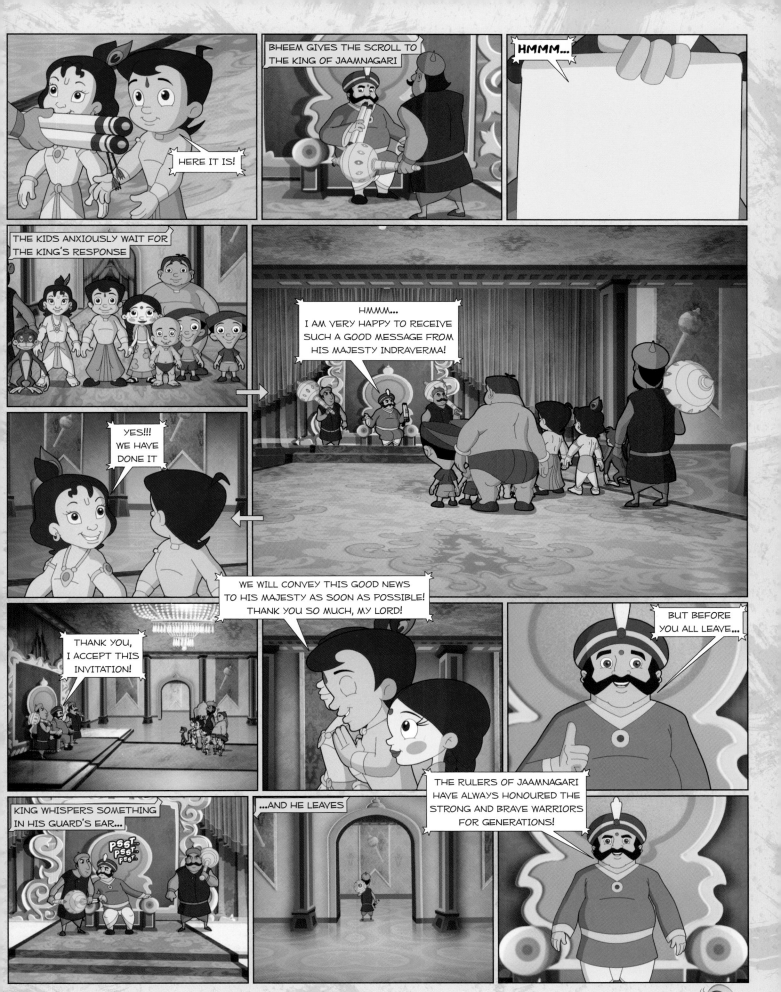

SOON THE GUARD COMES WITH SOMETHING HIDDEN IN HIS HANDS

IT IS A MATTER OF GREAT PRIDE TO US THAT A GREAT WARRIOR LIKE YOU HAVE COME TO MY COURTYARD!

AAH!!!

I WOULD LIKE TO GIVE THIS SPECIAL MACE TO YOU...

...AS A GIFT FROM US!

THANK YOU, MY LORD!

I REQUEST YOU ALL STAY BACK THIS NIGHT AND LEAVE FOR DHOLAKPUR TOMORROW MORNING!

PLEASE ENJOY OUR HOSPITALITY TILL THEN!

ALL ARE HAPPY AND AGREE TO STAY BACK

NEXT MORNING

WOW, JAAMNAGARI WAS INDEED A FANTASTIC KINGDOM, GUYS!

RIGHT! AND EVEN THE KING WAS SO NICE AND KIND!

OH YES, HE SERVED SO MANY HOT AND CRISPY KACHORIES!

CHOMP

ALL YOU CAN THINK AND DISCUSS IS FOOD! HMPH! THE BEST THING ABOUT THIS PLACE WAS THAT WE COULD MEET SO MANY EXPERT MACE-WARRIORS!

AND THEY WERE ALL PRAISING ABOUT OUR MAJESTY'S WARFARE TECHNIQUES!

ZZZZZZZZZ

UH LOOK, RAJU SLEPT!

I AM FEELING SLEEPY TOO!

HUH!?

YOU GUYS LOOK SO TIRED!

WHY DON'T YOU ALL TAKE A QUICK NAP? WE WILL REACH DHOLAKPUR BY NIGHT!

YOU ARE RIGHT KANHA!

www.chhotabheem.com

ALL OF A SUDDEN THE WHIRLWIND FORMS IN THE SKY...

...AND THE WINDS STARTS BLOWING AT HIGH SPEED

WOOSH

WOOSH

HUH!?

I DON'T KNOW, THE WIND-SPEED HAS INCREASED SUDDENLY!

WHAT SORT OF NOISE IS THIS?

BHEEM, CAN YOU TELL US WHAT IS HAPPENING?

MAYBE BECAUSE IT IS A HILLY REGION, FRIENDS!

SWOOSH

SHIVER

OH GOD, WHAT DO WE DO NOW?

THE WIND IS JUST UNCONTROLLABLE

SWOOSH

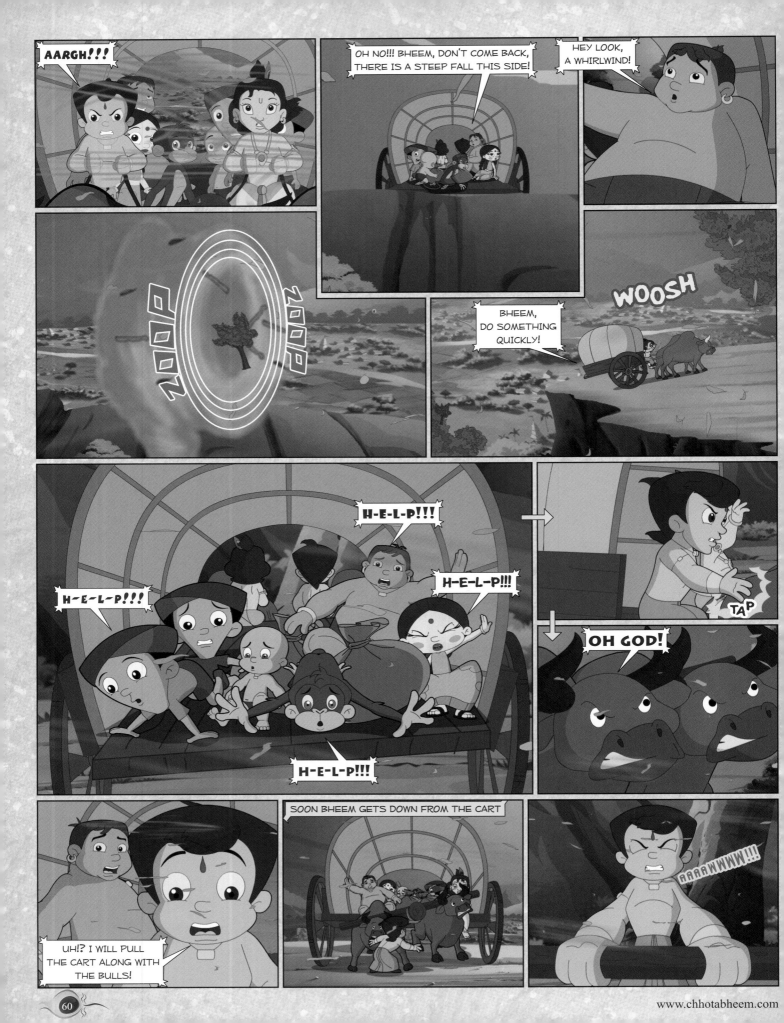

MEANWHILE THE WINDS ARE BLOWING IN FULL SPEED

HELP BHEEM!

BOTH KANHA AND BHEEM APPLY THEIR STRENGTH TO PULL THE CART

SWOOSH

OH NO, THIS WHIRLWIND WILL SWALLOW US!

PHOO

THE WIND'S PRESSURE IS SUCH THAT THE CART RISES FROM THE SURFACE

BHEEM! KANHA!

THE CART IS ALMOST RUINED

SWOOSH

OH!!! POOR BULLS

MAAAA

KANHA FREES THE BULLS AND SAVES THEM

WOOSH

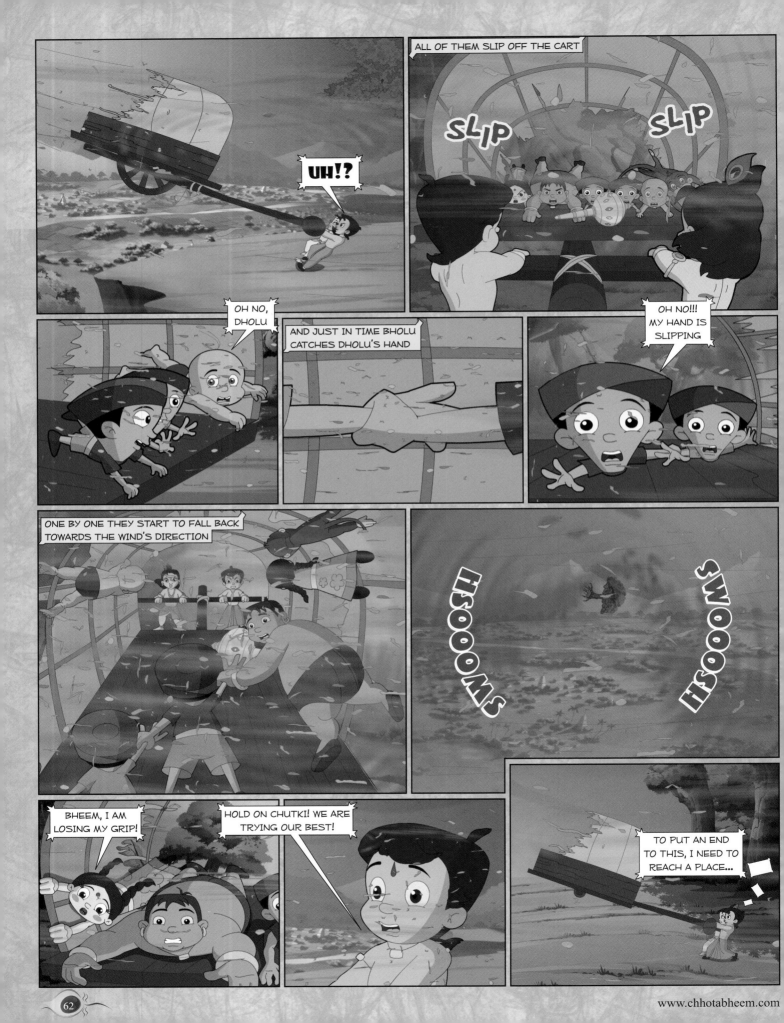

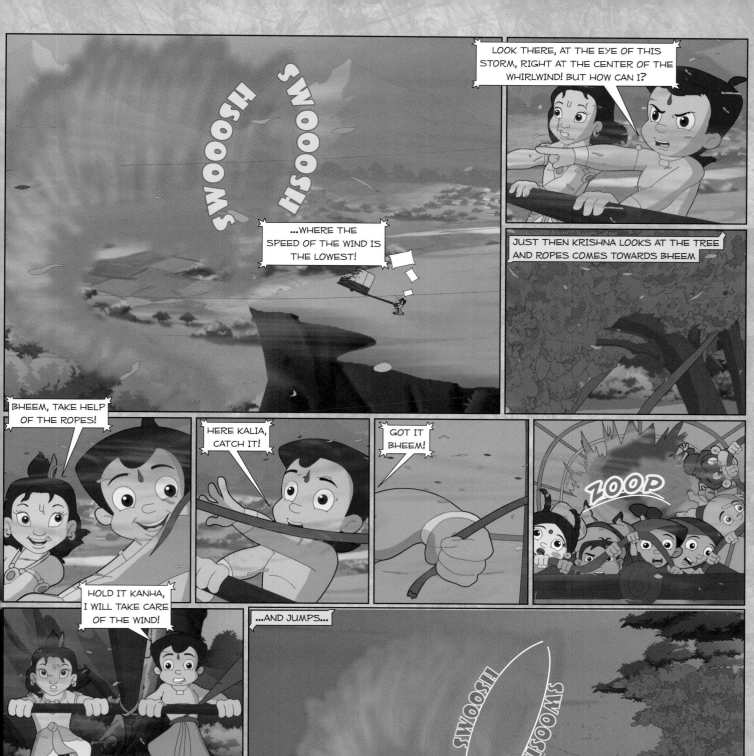

...INTO THE WHIRLPOOL

YAAAAH!

BHEEM HITS THE MACE WITH FULL FORCE

DDHAM

DON'T WORRY FRIENDS!

KANHA PULLS THE ROPE TOWARDS HIM...

AAAAWWWW!!!

...TO SAVE THE KIDS

UH!!!

AAAAWWWW!!!

AAHH!!!

SOON BHEEM TAKES CONTROL OVER THE WHIRLPOOL

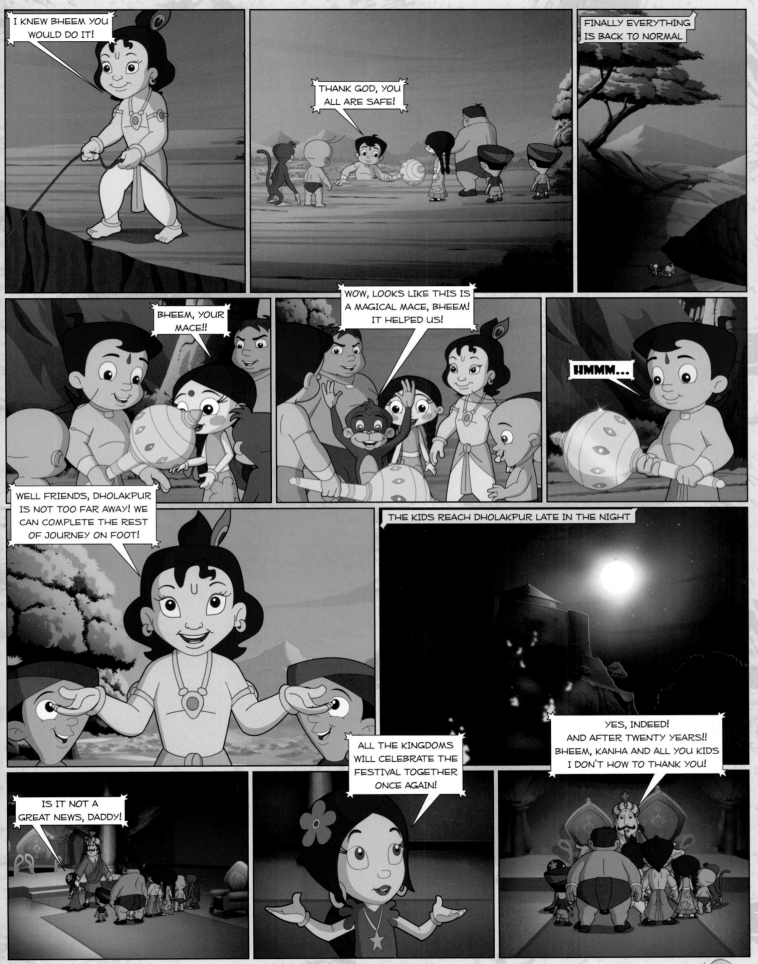

TOMORROW MORNING THE KINGS OF JAAMNAGARI, MAANIKDESH AND PORSINGHA WILL BE HERE AT DHOLAKPUR ALONG WITH THEIR WARRIORS...

YOU DON'T NEED TO THANK US, MY LORD! YOU RATHER START THE PREPARATIONS!

...TO CELEBRATE THE FOOD AND MIGHT FESTIVAL AT THE OLD STONE TEMPLE SITUATED NEAR THE BORDER OF DHOLAKPUR!

AT THE SAME OLD PLACE! OH, HOW WONDERFUL! I WILL ASK MY MEN TO GET TO WORK RIGHT AWAY!

AND I SUGGEST THAT ALL YOU KIDS TAKE REST AT THE PALACE TONIGHT!

WE WILL ALL LEAVE TOGETHER FOR THE STONE TEMPLE AT THE BREAK OF DAWN TOMORROW!

ALL ARE HAPPY WITH THE KING'S SUGGESTION

CLAP!!

COME, I WILL TAKE YOU TO THE GUEST ROOMS!

OKAY, LET'S GO!

IT IS A FULL MOON NIGHT AND EVERYTHING IS AT PEACE OUTSIDE THE PALACE OF DHOLAKPUR BUT...

...INSIDE THE PALACE KANHA AND BHEEM ARE AWAKE

ZZZZZZZ ZZZZZZZ ZZZZZZZ

TOMORROW IS GOING TO BE A VERY SPECIAL DAY!

OH YES, VERY SPECIAL AND IMPORTANT TOO!

KANHA, WHY AM I GETTING THIS FELLING THAT SOMETHING WRONG IS GOING TO HAPPEN?

IT IS YOUR SIXTH SENSE BHEEM WHICH IS WARNING YOU TO STAY ALERT! IT IS SAYING THAT THOUGH THE LIGHT OF THE FULL MOON WIPES AWAY THE DARKNESS...

...THE DARK DESIRES OF THE EVIL FORCES CAN STILL STRIKE ANYTIME!

ON THE OTHER SIDE KIRMADA IS OBTAINING POWERS IN FULL SWING

ha! ha! ha! ha!

KIRMADA, ALL MY DARK POWERS ARE YOURS NOW!

HA! HA! HA!

YES-S-S!

...COME OUT MARCHING TOWARDS KIRMADA

KIRMADA-KIRMADA! KIRMADA-KIRMADA! KIRMADA- KIRMADA! KIRMADA-KIRMADA! KIRMADA-KIRMADA! KIRMADA-KIRMADA! KIRMADA-KIRMADA! KIRMADA...!

KIRMADA, HA! HA! HA!

MOVE AHEAD! WIPE OUT BHEEM AND HIS BELOVED DHOLAKPUR FROM THIS EARTH!

NOW GET GOING!

MEANWHILE ON THE OTHER SIDE...

...THE PREPARATIONS TO WELCOME THE KINGS OF OTHER KINGDOMS...

...ARE ALMOST DONE

LOOK, THERE THEY COME!

AAH!!!

ALL THE THREE KINGS OF THE NEIGHBOURING KINGDOMS...

...MAANIKDESH...

...PORSINGHA AND...

...JAAMNAGARI...

...ARE WELCOMED WITH FULL HONOURS ALONG WITH THEIR ARMY

I WELCOME ALL OF YOU TO DHOLAKPUR!

HMPH!

HMPH!

HMPH!

I UH!?

HUH!?

OH!!! THEY DON'T LOOK HAPPY!

AND WHEN ALL OF THEM ARE PERPLEXED, THEN SUDDENLY

OLD FRIENDS SHOULD BE WELCOMED WITH A WARM HUG, INDRAVERMA...

REARRANGE THE PICTURE BELOW

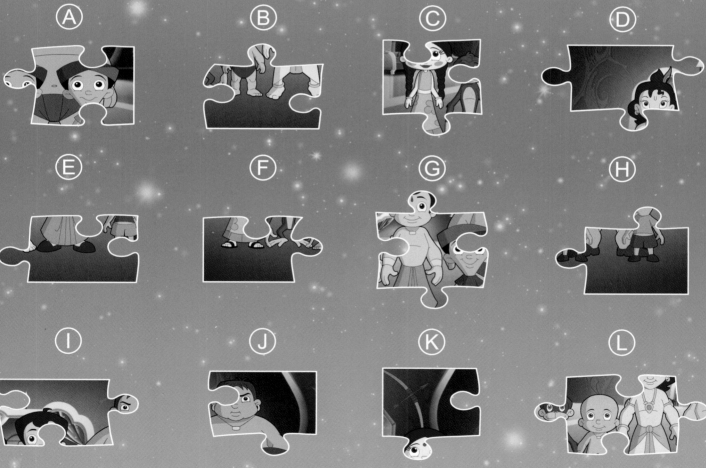

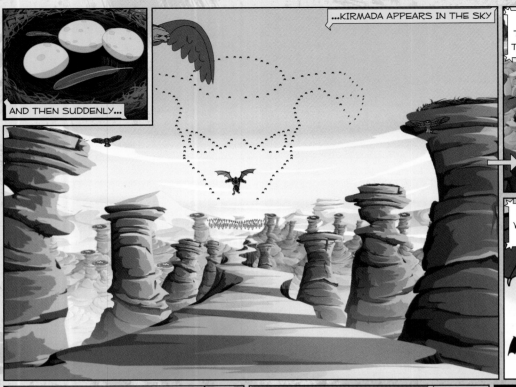

AND THEN SUDDENLY...

...KIRMADA APPEARS IN THE SKY

MY ARMY IS HUNGRY, THESE EGGS WILL FULFILL THEIR HUNGER. HA! HA! HA!

COME ON MY HUNGRY WARRIORS, HAVE SOME BREAKFAST!

OH NO!!!

KIRMADA THROWS THE EGGS TOWARDS THE EVIL SOLDIERS

THE BATS FLOCK TOGETHER AND...

FLAP!!!

FLAP!!!

FLAP!!!

...ATTACK THE NESTS

PUFF

SWOOSH

THE EVIL BATS OF KIRMADA DROP...

...THE EGGS AT THE MONSTERS

HA!

HA!

OH NO!!! LOOK, OUR EGGS!

THE EAGLES COME TO SAVE THEIR EGGS

YOU DROPPED MY EGGS, I WILL NOT SPARE YOU!

HEY, WHAT ARE YOU DOING?

THE EAGLES RAGE IN ANGER AND CHASE THE EVIL BATS

AARGH!!!

KIRMADA'S ARMY GOES TO KIRMADA FOR HELP

YOUR MAJESTY, PLEASE SAVE US FROM THESE BIG BIRDS!

HEARING HIS ARMY...

...KIRMADA RISES AND SENDS POWERFUL RAYS...

...TOWARDS THE EAGLES

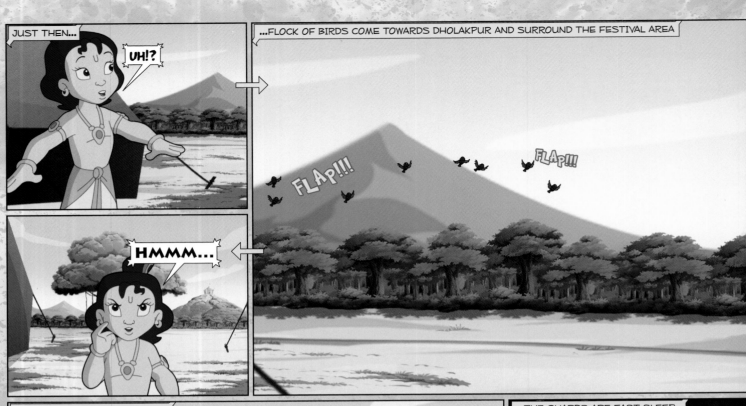

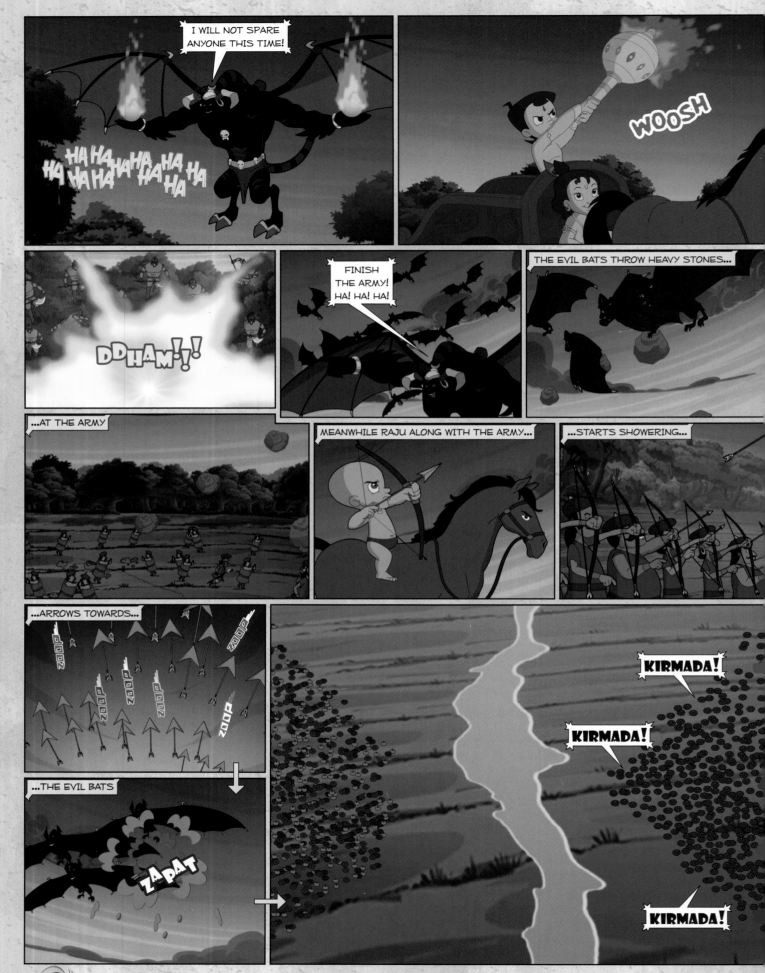

BOTH THE ARMIES STAND STARING AND ARE READY TO ATTACK

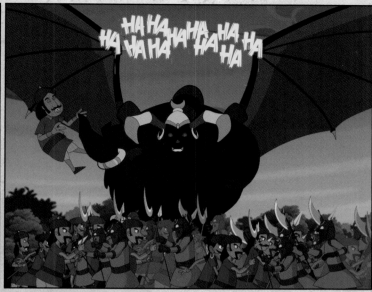

HELP!!!

THE EVIL GOBLINS START BITING THE ARMY

NO ONE SHOULD BE ALIVE!

JUST THEN A BAT LIFTS A SOLDIER...

HELP!!!

...AND DROPS HIM DOWN

DDHAM

THE OTHER KINGDOM'S KING TOO ATTACKS KIRMADA'S ARMY

ZOOP

ZAPAT

KALIA TOO TAKES CHARGE

GRRRR...

STAACK

OH NO, THEY ARE HEADING TOWARDS ME!

KALIA QUICKLY HITS THE EVIL BIRDS WITH HIS MACE

STAACK

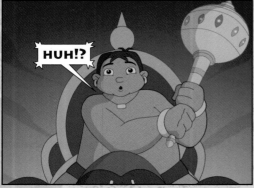

HUH!?

HELP!!!

DON'T WORRY KALIA, I WILL FIX THEM UP!

SHAK

RAJU PERFECTLY HITS...

SWOOSH

SWOOSH

...THE EVIL BIRDS

ZAPAK

88

www.chhotabheem.com

BHEEM RAISES HIS MACE...

...AND KEEPS DESTROYING THE MONSTERS

THE GREEN LIQUID COMES TOGETHER TO FORM A BIGGER MONSTER

HUH?!

AARGH!!!

THIS MONSTER IS SO HUGE!

THE MONSTER ATTACKS BHEEM...

...BUT BHEEM QUICKLY...

GRRR...

...THROWS HIS MACE AT THE MONSTER

DDHAM!!

WELL DONE, BHEEM!

MEANWHILE THE EVIL MONSTERS ARE JUST UNSTOPPABLE

TAK

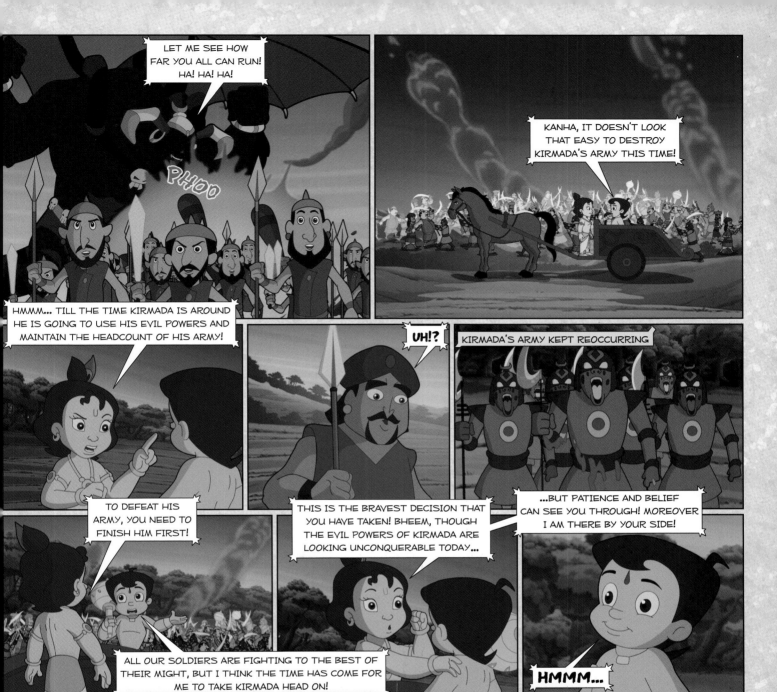

JUST IN TIME BHEEM JUMPS FROM THE CHARIOT

TRY TO ESCAPE THIS ONE, BHEEM!

CRASH

GRRR...

KIRMADA RAGES IN ANGER

AARGH!!!

MOUNTAIN LIKE MONSTERS COME AND...

...SURROUND BHEEM FROM ALL THE SIDES

TAK

THE GAME IS NOT OVER YET, KIRMADA!

WAIT TILL I TEACH YOU A LESSON!

HA! HA! HA! YOU CAN DO NOTHING TO ME!

ELECTRIFYING RAYS COMES FROM THE SKY AND...

RUMBLE RUMBLE

...AND PULL AWAY BHEEM'S MACE

HUH!?

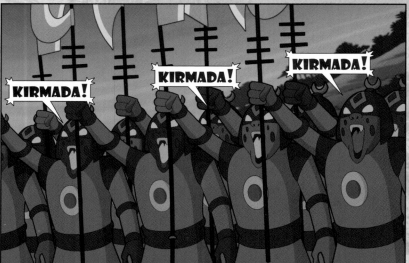

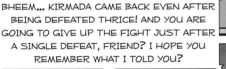

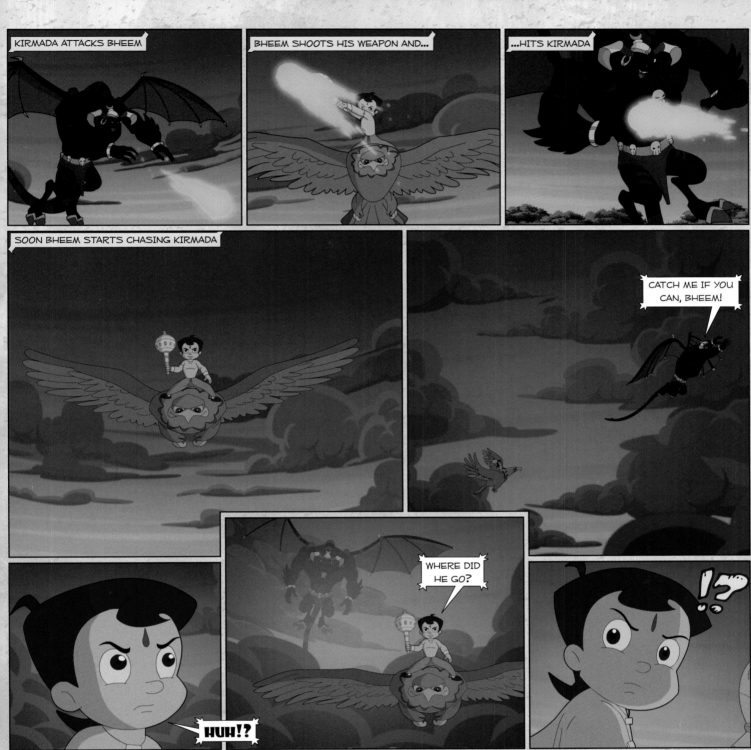

HA! HA! HA!

GRRR...

YOUR GAME IS OVER, KIRMADA!

BHEEM CATCHES KIRMADA'S TAIL AND PULLS HIM...

...AND SWINGS HIM AROUND

GRRR...

AARGH!!!

KIRMADA GATHERS ALL HIS POWER, MAKES A BALL OF FIRE...

...AND THROWS IT AT BHEEM

RUMBLE

SWOOSH

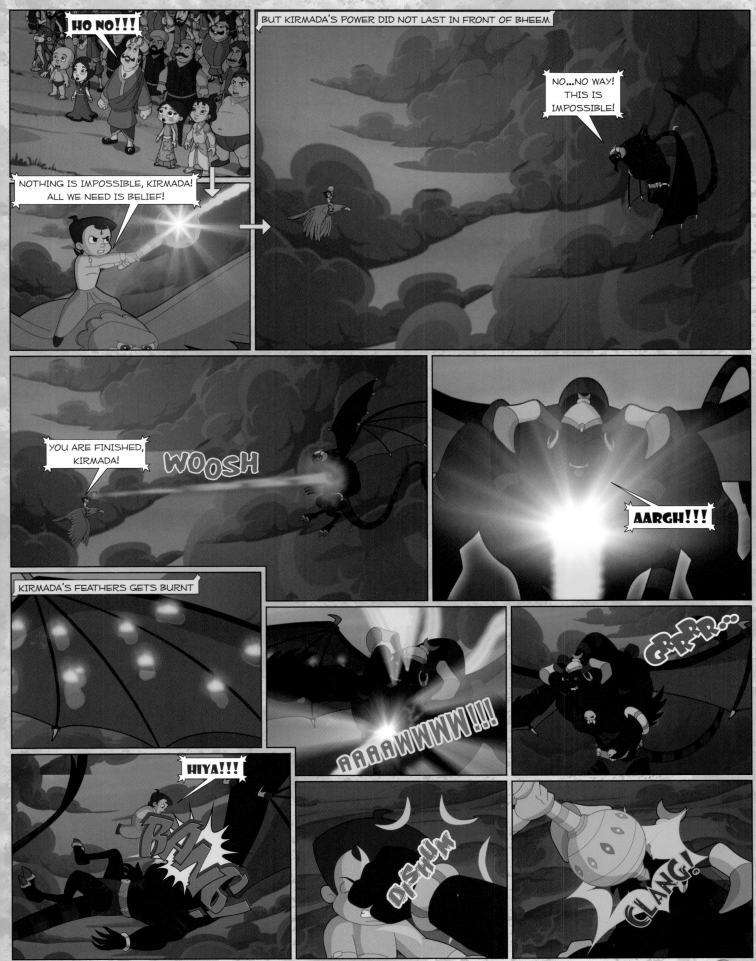

BHEEM HITS KIRMADA SO HARD THAT HE CRIES IN PAIN

AARGH!!!

OH NO, BHEEM!

BHEEM TAKES KIRMADA FAR AWAY AND...

...DESTROYS HIM

HUH!?

UH!?

TEARS ROLLS DOWN RAJU'S CHEEKS

BHEEM, SOB SOB!

HMPH!!!

A HUGE EXPLOSION TAKES PLACE...

DDHAM

...KIRMADA'S ARMY GETS DESTROYED

AND THEN SUDDENLY BHEEM COMES OUT OF THE EXPLOSION

SEEING BHEEM ALL OF THEM LOOK RELIEVED

VIOLENT RAYS EMITS FROM KIRMADA'S BODY

BHEEM LOOKS BEHIND TO SEE

THE RAYS DESTROY HIS ARMY

FINALLY THE RAYS OF SUNLIGHT FALL ON BHEEM

AS ALWAYS BHEEM WINS OVER EVIL

ONCE AGAIN THERE IS PEACE AND HAPPINESS IN DHOLAKPUR KINGDOM

HELP KALIA TO FIND DHOLU BHOLU BY MULTIPLICATION PROCESS WITH 2 TABLE

Help Kalia to find Dholu Bholu by Multiplication Process with 2 Table

		2	4	1	11	33	17
		5	6	17	31	19	49
9	19	15	8	10	43	21	35
33	17	3	7	12	38	13	41
41	14	44	16	14	23	49	1
3	28	5	18	15	23	15	47
37	34	21	20	22	24		
29	11	45	27	21	25		